Everyd~~ay Math~~

Written by Margie Burton, Ca

My grandma and I
got some seeds.

On Monday,
I went to the garden
with my grandma.

We put some seeds
in the soil.

On Tuesday,
I went to the garden
with my grandma.

We put some water
on the seeds.

On Wednesday,
I went to the garden
with my grandma.

We looked for
the seeds.

On Thursday,
I went to the garden
with my grandma.

We looked for
the sun.

On Friday,
I went to the garden
with my grandma.

The sun did not
come out.

On Saturday,
we did not go
to the garden.

On Sunday,
the seeds came up.